Woorayl

Helen Gibson

illustrated by Ninon Philips

Modern Curriculum Press
Cleveland and Toronto

In the forest, where tall gum trees reach up to the sky, lives Woorayl the lyrebird.

It is winter. Each morning when the first light creeps through the bush, Beleck-beleck, the lyrebird king of the forest, calls from his perch high in a tall tree to tell everyone this is his kingdom, his and Woorayl's.

Woorayl glides down to the ground. She digs for food. She rakes the earth with one strong claw, turning over bark and sticks. Her big dark eyes miss nothing. All the grubs and worms and other insects that live in the damp ground are good food for her.

She is not alone. A yellow robin watches from a tree trunk. Scrub wrens chatter near by. A pilot bird follows her. They are waiting for the insects that she leaves behind.

When the sun pokes long fingers through the trees and the mist, Woorayl stops feeding and stands on a log and preens. She runs her beak through each long feather.

From far away there comes a coughing bark. Woorayl listens with her crest raised. She knows it is Fox. He is hungry.

She fluffs and shakes her feathers and hops to the ground.

Suddenly the forest rings with the songs of many birds —
thrushes, whip birds, black cockatoos, kookaburras and
crimson rosellas. It is Beleck-beleck singing the songs of all
these birds.

He stops singing to rake sticks and leaves with strong claws.
He scratches the earth into a mound. He has many mounds like
this one.

He sees Woorayl. He calls "blick, blick" and runs toward her. She pretends she does not see him.

Beleck-beleck comes close to her. He sings softly and raises his wing up and down.

He runs back to the mound, calling to her again, "blick, blick." There is a whirring noise like a clock spring unwinding.

It is Beleck-beleck spreading his tail. It is like a shimmering silver curtain hiding him.

He jumps from one foot to the other, moving around the mound, "clonk, clonk."

Woorayl watches him from under the ferns. One day she will go on to the mound and under that silver tail and they will be like one bird.

But now she has other business. She runs through the bush and down a steep hill to where the creek sings a song as it tumbles over the rocks.

She walks into a quiet pool and splashes in the water. This is her bath. She stands on a log and preens, shaking her feathers to dry them.

She walks beside the creek looking for something. At last she finds it. It is a hollow in the side of the bank under the frond of a tree fern.

She picks up a stick and lays it in the hollow. She picks up another one and does the same. Soon there is a cradle of sticks.

She needs a big nest and she will have many days of hard work building it. She will gather bark and dead leaves and moss and fine roots to bind the sticks together. When the nest is finished she will put a spray of green gum leaves on top of it.

On the other side of the creek Fox listens and smells.

Woorayl leaves the nest to follow Beleck-beleck.

Six days pass. There is something in the nest. It is a large egg, Woorayl's egg.

All night she sits in the nest, her long tail curved around the back and side. She hears the song of the tumbling water below her. She hears the possums playing in the trees above her. A wombat scratches the earth in his burrow. Sometimes she

wakes in fear at a coughing bark across the creek. Fox is hunting.

When the first morning light creeps through the trees, Woorayl leaves the nest and scratches for food.

She feeds for a long time. Then she preens her feathers before she sits on her egg again. She can hear Beleck-beleck singing to her.

She stands on the step of the nest and looks in. She gives a sharp alarm call. The egg has gone. She does not see something creeping up behind her. Snap! Sharp teeth catch her tail.

Woorayl shrieks and pulls hard. Her tail feathers stay behind in Fox's mouth and she rushes through the bush.

Fox drops the feathers and shows his teeth. A lyrebird's egg is good, but a lyrebird would make a better meal.

Woorayl has lost her tail and her egg. Her tail will grow again in the spring but she will not lay another egg this year. Not until next winter will she build another nest.

Again it is winter. Woorayl finds a very secret place for her nest. It is on the top of a sloping tree fern trunk. She gathers sticks to make the cradle of the nest. She builds up the back and the sides and the top with more sticks. She gathers moss and rootlets and dead leaves to bind it together.

Far away, Beleck-beleck is singing to her. When the nest is finished she wanders through the forest with him. She feeds with him. He calls her with many blicks. At last she goes on to a mound with him and under the silver curtain of his tail. And they are like one bird.

Woorayl lays her egg in the new nest. She broods it for many days and nights. Six weeks pass.

She covers the egg with soft feathers she pulls from her sides. She can hear a faint tapping inside the egg. It is the baby lyrebird pushing its way into the world.

The egg cracks and splits. Woorayl throws out the bits of egg shell. She looks down at what is nestling in the feathers. It is a little gray bundle with closed eyes and big feet and bits of hairy down sticking out of its head and body.

It is Golgol the young lyrebird.

After a few days his eyes open. He is covered in sooty down. He is always hungry. Woorayl feeds him with wriggling worms and other insects. As she comes to the nest she calls to him with a soft crooning noise. At night she keeps him warm under her feathers.

He grows fast. Soon there is no room in the nest for Woorayl. She roosts in a nearby tree.

Golgol fills the nest. His feathers grow. He stands up and stretches his little wings.

Woorayl is away gathering food. Golgol hears a strange noise. Something is creeping, scratching, coming nearer.

His heart goes *pit-a-pat* very fast. He peers out. There is a shadow above him. Something big and black is on the trunk near the nest.

Golgol shrieks. He pushes out of the nest and tumbles to the ground. The wild cat looks down at him, ready to spring.

Woorayl comes rushing through the bush. Her crest is up and her wings are spread. She flies at the cat with her claws out. It runs off into the bush.

Woorayl makes Golgol follow her. His legs are wobbly and he falls over. Woorayl hides him under a big log. When night comes she shows him how to hop and scramble up the branches of a tree until he is high and safe. They hear a coughing bark. Fox is hunting. The wild cat hunts too.

Golgol grows quickly. He learns to fly. He follows his mother, making soft crying noises. She fills his beak with food. He learns to dig and find food for himself.

It is summer. They wander far in the forest. Golgol finds other young lyrebirds and they play together. They chase one another in and out and round about the ferns and logs and trees.

When the first rain has fallen in autumn, Golgol hears something that makes him stand still and listen. It is as if all the birds of the forest are singing.

He moves closer to the sound and looks through the ferns and sword-grass. He sees the most beautiful sight he has ever seen. It is Beleck-beleck, hidden under his shimmering silver tail, singing.

Golgol tries to sing. He cannot sing and he has no beautiful tail. But he will learn from Beleck-beleck.

Spring, summer, autumn and winter come and go many times.

Each spring as Golgol's tail feathers moult new ones grow and some are silver.

Woorayl has new nests and new babies to care for.

It is winter. When the sun pokes long fingers through the trees and mist, it shines on a new mound.

On the mound a lyrebird is moving round and round. He is covered with the silver curtain of his beautiful tail. The forest rings with his song.

It is Golgol. He is a king of the forest.

Note: The names 'Woorayl', 'Beleck-beleck', and 'Golgol', are Aboriginal words for 'Lyrebird'.